Introduction

The activities in the book provide ongoing
Number. They are short, snappy, fun activ
in the following contexts:

- between lessons
- before play
- before going home
- before assembly
- first thing in the morning
- during PE
- during informal 'on the rug' sessions
- after more formal written mathematics
- before introducing the next mathematical topic
- as revision and rehearsal.

The idea behind this book is that the activities provide a means of
keeping a numerical concept, skill or operation 'on-the-go' (i.e.
simmering) and alive in the children's minds. In order to become
numerate adults, children need to develop and refine their
mental techniques with numbers. These simmering activities
allow children to practise their strategies in the context of a game
or other fun activity.

It is clear that a major factor in helping children to develop a real
mental facility with numbers is the presence of regular activities.
The golden rule is 'little and often'. Children will enjoy a quick
game played on the rug or while they are waiting to go into the
hall for assembly. Some games become real favourites and
children will ask to play them repeatedly.

The simmering activities are categorised under topic headings for
easy access. Some games are playable at a variety of levels – with
lower numbers in Abacus R or Abacus 1 and with higher numbers
in Abacus 2. Many of the activities are readily adaptable to a
slightly different number context. All the activities are related to
the relevant Teacher Cards and units of work in Abacus.

Some of the activities in this book use materials such as number
cards, number grids etc., which can be found in the Abacus
Resource Packs.

Contents

Unit References

Abacus R	Section	Abacus 1	Section	Abacus 2	Section
N1 Numbers to 6	**1**	N1 Numbers to 10	**3**	N1 Addition	**7**
N2 Numbers to 6	**1**	N2 Addition	**8**	N2 Addition	**7, 8**
N3 Numbers to 6	**1**	N3 Numbers to 20	**2**	N3 Numbers to 20	**3**
N4 Numbers to 10	**1**	N4 Pattern	**7**	N4 Subtraction	**14**
N5 Numbers to 10	**1**	N5 Addition	**7**	N5 Numbers to 100	**5**
N6 Ordinal numbers	**4**	N6 Numbers to 20	**2, 22**	N6 Addition	**8, 9**
N7 Numbers to 10	**3**	N7 Sorting	**–**	N7 Numbers to 100	**5, 24**
N8 One more	**1**	N8 Fractions	**28**	N8 Addition	**8**
N9 One more	**1**	N9 Addition	**6, 8**	N9 Subtraction	**14**
N10 Counting on	**6**	N10 Taking away	**14**	N10 Multiplication	**23, 29**
N11 Counting back	**1**	N11 Numbers to 30	**2, 22**	N11 Pattern	**29**
N12 Ordering	**1**	N12 Block graph	**–**	N12 Sorting	**–**
N13 Ordering	**1**	N13 Numbers to 100	**5, 24**	N13 Numbers to 100	**5, 11, 23**
N14 Ordering	**1**	N14 Pictograph	**–**	N14 Numbers to 100	**11, 15, 21**
N15 Sorting	**–**	N15 Numbers to 100	**5**	N15 Addition	**10, 12**
N16 Pattern	**29**	N16 Numbers to 100	**5, 24**	N16 Numbers to 100	**25**
N17 Addition	**6**	N17 Subtraction	**19**	N17 Multiplication	**23, 29**
N18 Counting on	**6**	N18 Addition	**7**	N18 Multiplication	**23, 29**
N19 Addition	**6**	N19 Sorting	**–**	N19 Division	**26**
N20 Sorting	**–**	N20 Addition	**8**	N20 Difference	**20**
N21 Numbers to 20	**2**	N21 Numbers to 100	**5, 11, 24**	N21 Sorting	**–**
N22 Taking away	**14**	N22 Numbers to 100	**5, 10, 11**	N22 Block graph	**–**
N23 One less	**1, 14**	N23 Numbers to 100	**5, 15, 21**	N23 Negative numbers	**18**
		N24 Subtraction	**14**	N24 Addition	**10**
		N25 Subtraction	**14**	N25 Addition	**10**
		N26 Numbers to 100	**5**	N26 Subtraction	**15, 16**
		N27 Numbers to 100	**5, 24**	N27 Fractions	**27, 28**
				N28 Numbers to 1000	**17**
				N29 Numbers to 1000	**17**
				N30 Numbers to 1000	**17**

Section **1**: Counting to 10

Abacus R
N1, N2, N3, N4, N5, N8, N9, N11, N12, N13, N14, N23

- **Three, two, one, blast off!**
  Class activity
  With the children sitting, count in unison slowly and clearly up to ten and back from ten.
  On the way down the children get ready to jump: *...three, two, one, blast off*. The children jump up in the air like a rocket taking off.
  Repeat this activity often – at least twice a day for a while.
  Children gain immensely from counting in unison like this.
  Extend to counting to twenty when the children are ready.

- **Pinned on me!**
  Paper and pencil, sticky tape
  Class activity
  Write a number between 1 and 10 and stick it to a child's back so the other children can see it. They give the first child clues about the number without using its name. For example, they may say 'It's less than 5' or 'It's only got straight lines' or 'It's Jo's favourite number'.
  How quickly can the first child guess the number? Repeat with another child.

- **Finger count-up**
  Class activity
  This is a good activity for an assembly. Count in unison to ten, holding up one finger for each number spoken, so at *ten* all ten fingers are standing up. Then count down from ten, folding down one finger for each number spoken. Practise doing this quickly. How fast can the class count? Co-ordinating fingers with counting is difficult, and takes practice.

- **Target number**
  Class activity
  Ask the children to sit in a circle. Agree a target number, e.g. 7.
  Count around the circle from one, children taking turns to say
  a number. When ten is reached, start counting again at one.
  Any child who says the target number must stand up.
  Continue until five children are standing.

- **Quack, quack...**
  Class activity
  Ask the children to sit in a circle. The children take turns to
  choose an animal and make the appropriate number of noises.
  For example, the first child quacks once, the second child
  miaows twice, the third child barks three times, and so on up
  to ten.
  Count down from ten in the same way. Ensure everyone has a
  turn. The children can suggest animals.

- **One more or one less**
  Class activity
  Ask the children to sit in pairs and tell them stories involving
  'one less' or 'one more'. For example:
  *Five big, hairy spiders march across the teacher's desk. One falls on
  the floor. How many are still on the desk?*
  *There were three big, muddy puddles. Tom fell in one and sat down!
  Amy fell in the other and sat down! How many puddles are left?*

- **Counting songs**
  Class activity
  Sing counting songs with the children. Encourage the children
  to use their fingers to represent the numbers in these songs.

  Once I caught a fish alive
  One, two, three, four, five
  Once I caught a fish alive
  Six, seven, eight, nine, ten
  Then I let it go again

  Why did I let it go?
  Because it bit my finger so
  Which finger did it bite?
  This little finger on my right.

One man went to mow

One man went to mow
Went to mow a meadow
One man and his dog, Spot,
Went to mow a meadow.

Two men went to mow
Went to mow a meadow
Two men, one man and his dog, Spot
Went to mow a meadow.

Three men went to mow...

Alice the camel

*This is sung to the tune of 'dem bones, dem bones' and is a simple
counting-down rhyme for very young children*
Alice the camel has three humps
Alice the camel has three humps
Alice the camel has three humps
So go, Alice, go.

Boom, boom, boom...

Alice the camel has two humps
Alice the camel has two humps
Alice the camel has two humps
So go, Alice, go.

Boom, boom, boom...

Alice the camel has one hump
Alice the camel has one hump
Alice the camel has one hump
So go, Alice, go.

Boom, boom, boom...

Alice the camel has no humps
(*pause*)
Because Alice is a horse!

Section 2: Counting to 20

Abacus R
N21

Abacus 1
N3, N6, N11

• Count on...
Class activity
Point to a child who starts counting, slowly, loudly and clearly. Point to a different child. The first child immediately stops and the second continues counting. Point to a third child. The second child immediately stops, and the third continues counting. When the children reach an agreed target, e.g. 20, they must start counting backwards.
The children should be ready to take over counting at any time, so they must listen carefully.

• Guess which one?
Class activity
Tell the children that you have a number less than 12 in your pocket. They have three chances to guess which number it is. You can only answer 'yes' or 'no'.
For example, they may ask, 'Is it less than 6?', or 'Does it have two digits?'
When they have guessed yours, the children can take turns to choose a number. Encourage the children to think about their questions, e.g. 'Is it even?'

• Bigger than, smaller than
Class activity
Give the children two numbers, e.g. 4 and 16. They must name three numbers which are between these two limits (i.e. more than 4 and less than 16).
Repeat, letting the children take turns to choose the limits, e.g. more than 6 and less than 15.
Make the activity more difficult by allowing only non-consecutive numbers. For example, with limits more than 9 and less than 16: *ten, twelve and fourteen* is acceptable but not *ten, eleven, twelve.*

• Special number
Class Activity
Ask the children to sit in a circle. Choose a 'special' number,
e.g. 4. Count around the circle from one, children taking turns
to say a number. When twenty is reached, start counting again
at one. Any child who says the special number must stand up.
Continue until seven children are standing.

• Clapping the numbers
Ask the children to sit in a circle. They take turns to count by
clapping the number. So, the first child claps once, the second
child claps twice, the third child claps three times, and so on
up to 20.
This is difficult for the larger numbers. The children must
concentrate to check that the correct number has been
clapped.

• Before and after
Class activity
Choose a child. Say a number, e.g. *six*. That child has to say the
number one after, i.e. *seven*. The first child then chooses
another child, and says a number. Continue, with children
saying a number then choosing another child.
Variation: Play with children saying the number one before.
Play with boys saying the number **after** the number given,
and girls saying the number **before**.

• Twos counting
Class activity
The children take turns to count in twos from one. So, the first
child says 'one', the second says 'three', the third says 'five',
and so on. Help the children by telling them to miss out one
number each time.
Count in twos starting at two. This is often easier.
Count backwards in twos, starting at twenty-one. This is more
difficult.

Section 3: Number names

Abacus R
N7

Abacus 1
N1

Abacus 2
N3

- **Flash cards**
  Large flash cards numbered 1 to 10 with the matching
  number names on the reverse
  Class activity
  Hold up a card with the number name showing and ask the
  children to call out the number. Turn over the card. Were they
  correct?
  Variation: Place the cards in a feely bag. Ask a child to remove
  one, but before they do so ask the class to guess what the
  number will be. The first child removes the card and shows the
  class the number name. Was the guess correct?

- **Letter sort**
  Number cards (1 to 10), one for each child in the group, a
  board to write on
  Give each child a card. Say, 'Anyone holding a number which
  begins with a 't' stand up', or, 'Anyone holding a number with
  five letters in its name, stand up', or 'Anyone holding a
  number which ends in 'e'...' etc. Check each time by writing
  the relevant number names on the board.

- **Counting names**
  Number-name cards (one to ten)
  Ask the children to sit in a circle. Give each child a card. Count
  around the circle from one, children taking turns to say a
  number: *One, two, three, ...* When you reach ten, start again at
  one.
  Every third number in the chant, that child stands facing the
  circle, i.e. at *three, six, nine* in the first round. Continue
  counting: *Ten, one, two, ...* The child who says *two* stands up.
  Continue counting until all the children are standing in a line.

• Team up

Number cards (1 to 20), number name cards (one to twenty)

Deal out the number name cards, one per child. Divide the children into two teams according to a rule, e.g. numbers less than ten/numbers ten or more, or even numbers/odd numbers. Divide the number cards (1 to 20) in the same way. Shuffle each set and place them face down in two piles.

One child from each team turns over the top card in their pile, and says the number aloud. The child holding the matching number name in each team gives it to the child with the number card. The first team to do this scores a point.

A different child from each team turns over the next card in their pile and play continues. When all the cards are turned over and paired up, which team has the most points?

• Number shout

Number cards (1 to 20), number name cards (one to twenty)

Give out the number name cards, one to each child and place the number cards face up on the table. Ask the children to sit in a circle with the numbers in order.

The first child starts by shouting a number (not their own). The child with that number name collects the matching number card from the table. That child then shouts out another number and play continues.

Continue until everyone has two cards: a name and its matching numeral.

If a child shouts a number which is already taken he or she answers a question as a forfeit, e.g. *say the number after 6, say the number before 19.*

Section **4**: Ordinal numbers

Abacus R
N6

- **Highest first**
  Three rosettes labelled '1st', 2nd' and '3rd', one dice per child
  On a count of three, the children all throw their dice. Any child with a six stays in the game. Those children throw again. The child with the highest number (e.g. 6) is first, the child with the next largest number (e.g. 5) is second and the person with the third largest number is third. If more than one child has particular number they throw again until there is a clear first, second and third. Give the rosettes to the appropriate children.
  Repeat with every child throwing their dice.

- **First to fifth**
  Cubes
  Ask the children to sit in a circle. In unison count in ordinals around the circle, pointing to each child in turn: *first, second, third...* Instead of saying 'fifth' the fifth child takes a cube and stands up. Start again at 'first' with the next child, and continue until you reach 'fifth'. Again this child takes a cube and stands up. Continue in this way, missing out any child standing with a cube. Finally all the children except one should be standing. That child is the winner and takes two cubes.
  Repeat starting at a different place in the circle. Play several times or until someone has collected five cubes.

- **First to last**
  Cubes, a dice
  Ask the children to line up from first to sixth. Throw the dice. If you throw a three give the third child in each line a cube. Throw the dice again. If you throw a six, give the sixth child a cube. Continue throwing the dice and giving cubes to the matching children. Stop when every child in the line has at least one cube. Each child counts his or her cubes. The child who has the most stands first in the line. The child who has the second largest number stands second, and so on.
  Take back all the cubes and repeat.

Section 5: Counting to 100

Abacus 1
N13, N15, N16, N21,
N22, N23, N26, N27

Abacus 2
N5, N7, N13

- **Which number?**
  A board to write on
  Class activity
  Write the numbers 0 to 50 on the board like this:

Ask the class to choose a number, while you turn away,
without telling you what it is. You have four questions to guess
which number it is, for example: 'Is the number less than 25?',
'Does it have a '2' in it?'. The children can only answer 'yes' or
'no'.
When you guess the number choose another for the children
to guess.
Three children can leave the room while the other children
choose a number. Then they have four chances to guess it.
Continue with groups of three children taking turns to leave
the room.

- **Betwixt and between**
  Number cards (1 to 100)
  Class activity
  Give out a random selection of number cards (1 to 100), one
  per child. Choose two of the remainder, e.g. 45 and 60. Any
  children with a number between 45 and 60 stand up, and say
  their numbers aloud.
  Choose two new cards and repeat. Continue, letting the
  children choose the cards.

Target counting

Two dice

Class activity

Divide the children into two teams. Team A choose a target number, e.g. 50. Team B throw the two dice, e.g. 4 and 3 and make a two -digit number, e.g. 34. Team B count in unison from that number to the target number without making a mistake. If the target number is less than the dice number, they count backwards. If they count correctly they score a point. Team B then choose a target number and Team A throw the dice. Repeat several times.

One-legged race

Class activity

Ask the children to sit in a circle. Count around the circle to 100, children taking turns to say one number each. Any child who says a number ending in 5 or 0 stands up. If they are already standing, they stand on one leg.

Continue up to 100. How many people are standing up? How many are on one leg?

Repeat, starting with a different child.

Two's hard, three's even harder

Class activity

Ask the children to sit in a circle. Count round the circle in twos, children taking turns to say one number each: *two, four, six, ...* Vary the starting number, e.g. starting at 23: *twenty-five, twenty-seven, twenty-nine, ...*

Count in threes. Tell the children to say the missing two numbers softly to themselves to help. For example, the first child says *five*, the second child whispers *six, seven* and says *eight* aloud, the third child whispers *nine, ten* and says *eleven* aloud and so on.

Bingo

Pencil and paper for each pair, a ten-sided dice (numbered 0 to 9)

The children work in pairs. Each pair draws five circles on the page and writes a two-digit number in each. Throw the dice twice and make two two-digit numbers. For example, for throws of 3 and 2 make 32 and 23. Call out these numbers. If any pair have a matching number they can cross it out.
The winners are the first pair to cross out all their numbers.

One more than...

Class activity

The first child chooses another and says a number, e.g. *fifty-six*. The second then says the number which is 'one more', i.e. *fifty-seven*. If correct, the second child choose another child and says a number, e.g. *eighty*. That child responds immediately with *eighty-one*.

The most difficult numbers are those ending in 'nine'.

The game can be varied with children saying 'one less than' or 'two more than'.

Which numbers?

Class activity

Give the children simple problems, such as: *Name three numbers which are more than 24 and less than 42.*

Section 6: Addition: Counting on to 10

Abacus R
N10, N17, N18, N19

Abacus 1
N9

- **Story time**
  Class activity
  Ask the children to sit in pairs and tell them stories involving simple additions. For example:
  My cat had three kittens. How many cats do I have in total?
  Fred's Mum gave him three sticky buns. Then his Dad gave him two more. How many has he got now?
  There were five racing cars at the starting line and three more drove up. How many cars were ready to go?
  Can the children make up their own?

- **Dice count-on**
  Number cards (1 to 10) enough for one per child, a dice
  Class activity
  Deal one card to each child. Throw the dice. The children add the dice number to their card numbers. Choose a child. *What is your answer?* If correct, that child throws the dice. The children complete the additions and the dice-thrower chooses a new child. *What is your answer?*
  Continue until everyone has taken a turn.

- **Three more**
  Class activity
  Choose a child, and say a number, e.g. *four*. That child responds by saying the number three more, i.e. *seven*. The first child chooses a second child and says a different number. The second child again says three more, and chooses another child. Continue until everyone has taken a turn.
  Variations include 'two more', 'four more' or 'five more'.

Section **7**: Addition: Number bonds to 10

Abacus 1
N4, N5, N18

Abacus 2
N1, N2

- **Tower pairs**
  Interlocking cubes
  Make sets of towers, two or three for each number 1 to 9. Each tower should be a single colour. Place them on a table. Each child chooses a tower and finds a partner to make 10. For example, if Tom chooses a tower of four cubes, he needs a partner tower of six cubes.
  Replace the towers and play again, children choosing different towers.

- **Whoops-a-daisy!**
  Class activity
  Choose a child and 'throw' a number at them, e.g. *four*. That child must reply **immediately** by saying the number which makes ten, i.e. *six*. If correct, the first child chooses a second and says a number. That child must respond immediately with the number which makes ten. If any child can't respond immediately, he or she has 'fallen over': *Whoops-a-daisy!* It helps if boys choose girls and girls choose boys.

• Bus problems!
Class activity
Ask the children to sit in pairs and tell them 'bus' stories involving addition of three numbers. For example:
A bus has two fat men on it. It arrives at the first stop and two fat ladies get on. At the second stop four skinny children get on. How many people are there on the bus?

• Back-hands
Class activity
Divide the class into two teams. Team A collects numbers less than ten, Team B collects numbers more than ten.
Ask one child from each team to stand in front of the class, with both hands behind their backs. The whole class counts: *One, two, three, go!* Both children show their hands with some fingers standing up and some folded down. The class count the total number standing up. For example, one child might have four fingers standing up, and one might have seven fingers standing up, making eleven in total. In this case, Team B would score a point.
If the total is exactly ten, both teams get five points.
Repeat with another two children.
The game works well with the class playing against you, especially if you collect numbers less than ten!

• Clapping for ten
When dismissing children, choose one child. Clap three times. That child completes the ten by clapping seven times. Choose another child and clap five times. Continue, choosing different children.
A variation involves the children taking turns to choose a friend and clapping a number at them. The friend must complete the ten claps.

Section **8**: Addition: Counting on to 20

Abacus 1
N2, N9, N20

Abacus 2
N2, N6, N8

- **I went to market...**
A board to write on
The children take turns to speak. The first child says: 'I went to market and I bought a mango'. The second child says: 'I went to market and I bought a mango and two apples'. The third child says: 'I went to market and I bought a mango, two apples and three bananas'.
Continue, drawing each set on the board: one mango, two apples, three bananas...
How many things have been bought after six trips?

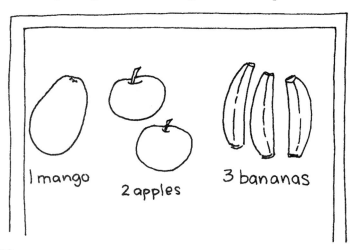

- **Dice pass-on**
A ten-sided dice
Class activity
The class play as a team against you. Choose a child and give him or her the dice. Say a number between 10 and 20, e.g. *seventeen*. The child repeats the number aloud and throws the dice, counting on the number shown. If correct, the dice is passed to another child and the class score a point.
Otherwise, you take the dice back and score a point.
Continue as long as it is fun.

- **Bag of coins**
  A feely bag, twenty 1p coins and several 10p coins
  Class activity
  Choose a child to take one 10p coin and several 1p coins from the bag. The child holds them up and the children agree the amount. A second child takes a few 1p coins, counts them and tells the class the amount.
  How much has been taken from the bag in total? Ask two children in the class for the answer. If they are correct, they take a turn to remove the coins from the bag.
  Repeat several times to give as many children as possible a turn.

- **Team-up**
  A dice
  Class activity
  Divide the children into two teams – it is important that the teams are evenly matched in terms of ability.
  One child from each team says a starting number between 11 and 20, e.g. 13 and 17. Both teams repeat their numbers aloud. Throw the dice, e.g. 5. Each team counts on five from their starting number. The first team to call out a correct answer (i.e. 18 or 22) scores a point.
  Continue until one team has five points.
  The game can be played with more than two teams.

Section **9**: Adding three one-digit numbers

Abacus 2
N6

- **Team effort**
  Three dice
  Class activity
  Divide the children into two teams. Team A collects numbers ten or less, Team B collects numbers more than ten. Choose one child from each team. The two children and yourself each throw a dice. Together add the three numbers, starting with the largest. If the answer is more than ten, Team B scores a point. If it is ten or less, Team A scores a point.
  Continue, until all the children have taken a turn to throw the dice.

- **Three each way**
  Interlocking cubes
  Nine children make a series of towers from one to nine cubes tall - one each. They form groups of three where the towers make fifteen cubes in total. For example: 9 + 2 + 4, 8 + 6 + 1, and 7 + 3 + 5.
  Can they arrange themselves in a different way?

- **Adding Bingo**
  Paper and pencil for each pair, three dice
  Class activity
  The children work in pairs. Each pair draws three circles on the page and writes a number from 3 to 18 in each. Throw the three dice and call out the numbers. The children add the three numbers, starting with the largest. If any pair have a matching number they can cross it out. The winners are the first pair to cross out all their numbers.

- **Story addition**
  Class activity
  Tell the children stories involving addition, for example:
  The shark is feeling greedy. He eats three small sea-horses, two large flat-fish and then one octopus. How many things has he eaten?

Section **10**: Addition: Counting on to 30-40

Abacus 1
N22

Abacus 2
N15, N24, N25

- **Story count-up**
  Class activity
  Ask the children to sit in pairs and tell them stories involving addition. For example:
  Once upon a time there was a poor woodcutter's son. His mother gave him twelve beautiful bread rolls as he set out on his adventures. He had not gone very far when he met a rabbit with its foot stuck in a trap. He was a kind young man and so he set the rabbit free. The rabbit was very grateful. It told him that because he had been so nice, every time he saw a rabbit on his journey three more rolls would magically appear in his lunch-box!
  The young man had many adventures and travelled many miles. However, he was never hungry because he saw six rabbits. When he finally got home, he had no rolls left. How many had he eaten?

- **Turn-over**
  Lots of 10p and 1p coins, cubes, cards marked with prices (32p, 33p, ... 40p)
  Shuffle the price cards and place them face down in a pile. Each child takes coins to match an amount from 31 to 39 pence. Throw the dice. The children count on that number from their starting amounts. Turn over the top card on the pile. Any child with a matching total takes a cube.
  Replace the card on the bottom of the pile and repeat. Can anyone collect three cubes?

- **Count on**
  Class activity
  Ask the children to sit in a circle. Give the first child a starting number, e.g. *sixteen*. The child counts on four and says the answer, i.e. *twenty*. The next child must count on four more, and say the answer: *twenty-four*.
  Continue round the circle.
  Vary by counting on a different number, e.g. *five*, or allowing the children to choose the next child each time.

Section **11**: Addition: Counting on in tens

Abacus 1
N21, N22

Abacus 2
N13, N14

- **All the tens**
  Class activity
  Ask the children to sit in a circle and count in tens in unison:
  ten, twenty, thirty, etc.

- **Keep counting**
  Class activity
  Ask the children to sit in a circle. The first child says any
  number between 0 and 9, e.g. *seven*.
  The children take turns to add ten, until ninety-seven is
  reached. The next child chooses a new number between 0 and
  9 and the activity is repeated.

- **Counting together**
  Class activity
  Choose a starting number, e.g. twenty-four. Count on in tens
  in unison: *twenty-four, thirty-four, forty-four, ... one hundred and
  four.*
  Each time the children say a number, they should 'throw' out
  ten fingers (by starting with their hands 'shut' with all the
  fingers folded down, and opening all the fingers at once and
  holding them up).
  Choose different starting numbers.

- **Ten more**
  Class activity
  The class play as a team against you. Choose a child and say a
  number, e.g. *forty-five*. That child must respond immediately by
  saying the number 'ten more', i.e. *fifty-five*.
  If correct, the class score a point, and that child chooses
  another and says a new number. Otherwise, you score a point
  and choose a new child to give a number to.
  Continue, giving as many children as possible a turn.

Ten more or less bingo

Paper and pencil for each pair, number cards (1 to 100)
Class activity
Shuffle the cards and place them face down in a pile.
The children work in pairs. Each pair draws four circles on the
page and writes a number in each. Turn over the top card from
the pile and call out the number. If any pair have a number ten
more or ten less they can cross it out. The winners are the first
pair to cross out all their numbers.

Coin-dismissal

Lots of 10p and 1p coins
Class activity
When dismissing children, give them a handful of 10p and 1p
coins. They have to count and say the total amount. They
must then tell you what 10p more would be. If necessary they
can check by taking another 10p.

Section **12**: Adding 11, 12, 13

Abacus 2
N15

- **Market again**
  A board to write on
  The children sit in a circle. You begin by saying: 'I went to
  market and I bought a birthday card for 15p.' Choose a child
  to continue: 'I went to market and I bought a birthday card for
  15p, and a comic for 11p. I spent 26p in all.' The next child in
  the circle continues: 'I went to market and I bought a birthday
  card for 15p, a comic for 11p and a sticker for 12p. I spent 38p
  in all.' How far can you get?
  It might help to write down the amounts (but not the objects)
  on the board.

- **How much?**
  Large card: '12p more!'
  Class activity
  Give the children shopping situations involving addition.
  'All these items have gone up by 12p:
  'I am a pencil case and I used to cost 34p. How much am I
  now?'
  'I am a set of stickers and I used to cost 25p. Now how much
  do I cost?'
  Let the children make up their own.
  Variations involve using a '11p more!' or a '13p more!' card.

- **Circle add**
  Ask the children to sit in a circle. Give one child a starting
  number, e.g. *eleven.*
  Taking turns around the circle the children add 12 and say the
  answer aloud. For example, the first child says: *eleven,* and the
  second child says: *twenty-three,* the third child says: *thirty-five*
  and so on.
  When they go over one hundred, start again.

● Number grid whereabouts
Number grid (0 to 99)
Class activity
Ask two children to choose a number between 10 and 100 and write it on a piece of paper, without anyone else seeing.
The rest of the class guess the number by moving around the number grid. Choose a child to point to any starting number in the first row, e.g. 3. *If we add 11, where are we then on the grid?* Choose a child to point to the new number, i.e. 14. Ask the pair with the paper: *Is the number in this row?* If so, the class can start guessing which number it is. If not, add another 11. Choose another child to point to the new number, i.e. 25. Each time ask the children if the number is in this row. Repeat with different children choosing the target number. Demonstrate how to add 11 by moving down one row and along one space.

0	1	2	3	4	5	6	7	8	9
10	11	12	13	14	15	16	17	18	19
20	21	22	23	24	25	26	27	28	29
30	31	32	33	34	35	36	37	38	39
40	41	42	43	44	45	46	47	48	49
50	51	52	53	54	55	56	57		
60	61	62	63	64	65	66	67	68	69
70	71	72	73	74	75	76	77	78	79
80	81	82	83	84	85	86	87	88	89
90	91	92	93	94	95	96	97	98	99

Section **13**: Addition: Counting on 20, 30, etc.

Abacus 2
N24

- **Circle twenties**
  Class activity
  Ask the children to sit in a circle. Choose a starting number between 1 and 9, e.g. 5. The first child says: *five*, the second child adds 20 and says: *twenty-five*, the third child adds another 20 and says: *forty-five*.
  Continue round the circle. How far can the children get?
  Repeat with another number between 1 and 9.

- **Flash cards**
  A set of flash cards with one side 20 more than the other (e.g. 24 and 44, 35 and 55, 2 and 22, 89 and 109), lots of 10p coins
  Class activity
  Hold up the cards one at a time, showing the smaller number to the class. Choose a child. *What is the number on the back?*
  Give a 10p coin for a correct answer.
  Move through the cards fairly quickly. Try to give every child at least one turn.

- **Higher and higher**
  Class activity
  Starting at 14 count in unison aloud in twenties: *fourteen, thirty-four, fifty-four, seventy-four...* As the children count, encourage them to 'throw' two tens using their fingers. They can whisper the intervening 'ten'. How far can they get?
  Repeat with a different starting number, e.g. 12. What happens when you go over 100?
  Can you count together in thirties?

Section **14**: Subtraction: taking away

Abacus R	**Abacus 1**	**Abacus 2**
N22, N23	N10, N24, N25	N4, N9

- **Finger count down**
  A dice
  Class activity
  Ask the children to sit, each with ten fingers in the air. Choose one child to throw the dice and call out the number, e.g. *four*. The other children fold down that number of fingers. How many are left? Say the numbers aloud: *Ten take away four leaves six.*
  Start again with ten fingers in the air. Choose another child to throw the dice.

- **Story take-away**
  Class activity
  Tell the children stories involving taking away, for example:
  Five fat flippy fish went swimming. Two fell in a fishing net and were caught! How many were left? (The children can use five fingers to represent the five fish to help them solve the problem.)
  Eight space-monsters landed on earth. Two fell in the sea and drowned. How many survived?
  Five children got on a bus. One got off at the first stop. Another got off at the second stop. How many were left on the bus?

- **Track down**
  Twelve large sheets of paper, with large numerals 1 to 12, a dice
  Class activity
  Lay out the pieces of paper on the floor in a track, from 12 to 1. Choose one child to be the 'counter'. This child stands on 12. Choose another child to throw the dice. The other children take away the dice throw from 12 and call out the answer. The 'counter' moves back the number shown on the dice. Were the children correct?
  Choose another child to throw the dice. Continue until the 'counter' passes 1.
  Play again with a new 'counter'.

• I started with...

Class activity

Start by saying: 'I started with 20p and I bought something for 2p. Then I had 18p left.' Point to a child to continue: 'I started with 18p and I bought something for 3p, then I had 15p left.' If correct, that child chooses another to go on.

Continue until you have no money left. Start again, always with 20p. No-one is allowed to spend more than 4p at a time.

• Count down

Interlocking cubes, a dice

The children work in pairs to make a line of cubes (15, 16, 17, 18, 19 or 20 cubes long). Throw the dice. The children take away that number of cubes. How many are left in their line? Throw the dice again. Again the children take away a matching number of cubes.

Continue like this.

The winning pairs are those who reach exactly 0, (without going beyond 0).

The children can build new lines of cubes and the game can begin again.

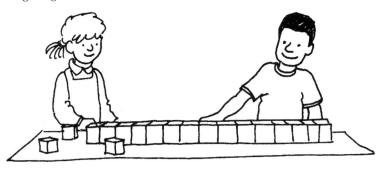

• Take-away race

Lots of 10p and 1p coins, dice (one for each group of three children)

The children work in threes and each group starts with 20p. They throw the dice as fast as they can and take away a matching number of 1p coins. This will involve exchanging their 10p coins for 1p coins. They continue throwing the dice and taking away.

Who reaches 0 first? (The children do not have to reach exactly 0, but they must get rid of all their coins.)

- **Hard cheese!**
  Cubes
  Class activity
  Divide the children into two teams. Choose a child from Team A, and ask a question such as: *What is seventeen take away nine?* That child should answer immediately. Choose a child from Team B and ask a similar question.
  Always ask a question which involves a 'teen' number take away **nine**. This should help children see the pattern, e.g. 1$\underline{4}$ take away 9 is $\underline{5}$ and so on. If any child doesn't respond immediately, then it's 'hard cheese' and he or she takes a cube. At the end, the team with the fewest cubes are the winners. Vary the game by taking away 8.

- **Songs**
  Class activity
  Sing songs with the children, which involve taking away. Encourage the children to use their fingers to represent the numbers in these songs.

Ten green bottles
Ten green bottles hanging on the wall
Ten green bottles hanging on the wall
And if one green bottle should accidentally fall
There'll be nine green bottles hanging on the wall

Nine green bottles...

Ten fat sausages
This is sung to the tune of 'Ten green bottles' but involves counting back two.
Ten fat sausages sizzling in the pan
Ten fat sausages sizzling in the pan
And if one goes pop and the other goes bang
There'll be eight fat sausages sizzling in the pan.

Eight fat sausages...

Section **15**: Subtraction: Counting back in tens

Abacus 1
N23

Abacus 2
N14, N26

- **Count down**
  Class activity
  Choose a child to say a number in the nineties, e.g. *ninety-six*.
  Together, the children count back in tens: *ninety-six, eighty-six, ...*
  Ask three children to stand and give them a starting number to
  count back from. The rest of the class check. Vary by asking all
  the boys to count back, or just those with black shoes on, ...

- **First to the line!**
  Paper and pencil for each child, cubes, a dice
  Class activity
  Each child writes a starting number between 50 and 100.
  Throw the dice and call out the number. The children count
  back a matching number of tens from their starting numbers.
  For example, if a child writes 78, and the dice shows 4, that
  child counts back four tens from 78 to 38. The children write
  the new numbers. Repeat several times.
  The winners are any children to reach a single-digit number,
  e.g. counting back 3 tens from 38. They **cannot** win by going
  beyond a single-digit number, e.g. counting back 4 tens from
  38. The winners take a cube. Play again.
  The overall winners are the children with the most cubes.

- **Up a row**
  Number grid (0 to 99), a ten-sided dice
  Class activity
  Throw the dice, to give a starting number in the nineties on
  the grid (e.g. throw a 4 start on 94, throw a 7 start on 97). Place
  your finger on that number, e.g. 97 and choose a child. That
  child counts back ten and says the number, i.e. *eighty-seven*.
  Move your finger up one row on the grid to 87. The first child
  chooses another child, who counts back ten and says the
  number, i.e. *seventy-seven*. Continue, with each child choosing
  the next who counts back ten.
  When you reach the top row, repeat the activity.

Section 16: Taking away two-digit numbers

Abacus 2
N26

- **Team difference**
  Number cards (20 to 100), a board to write on
  Divide the group into two teams. Choose a child from Team A to pick a card from the pack and read out the number, e.g. *forty-five*. Write the number on the board. The first child subtracts either 11, 12 or 13 mentally and says the answer aloud. Write the answer on the board. The other children in Team A must say whether 11, 12, or 13 has been subtracted. If they are correct Team A scores a point. Choose a child from Team B to pick a card.
  Continue playing so that each team member has a turn.

- **Flash cards**
  Flash cards with numbers on the front, and numbers 12 less on the reverse (e.g. 45/33, 76/64, 94/82)
  Class activity
  Show the children the front of a card. They subtract 12 mentally and say the answer. Wait until several children have offered an answer and then turn the card over. Were they correct? Vary this by aiming a card at a specific group of children: *This one is for Harry, Fred and Amie...*
  Aim some at the girls and some at the boys...

- **Money hand-over**
  Lots of 10p and 1p coins in a feely bag
  Class activity
  Choose a child to remove a handful of coins from the bag and count them out, e.g. 47p. That child turns to another and says: 'I'll give you all of this except 11p. How much will you have?' The second child must say the amount, i.e. 36p. The first child hands over all the coins except one 10p coin and one 1p coin. Was the second child correct? If so, that child replaces the coins, shakes the bag and takes a handful. The second child then chooses another and repeats the question.

Section **17**: Counting to 1000

Abacus 2
N28, N29, N30

- **Count-up**
  Class activity
  Choose a starting number (e.g. 234) and count round the class,
  children taking turns to say the next number: *two hundred and
  thirty-four, two-hundred and thirty-five, ...*
  Continue until everyone has said a number. Repeat with a
  different starting number.

- **Car numbers**
  A board to write on
  Class activity
  The children should collect as many car numbers as they can.
  Start by asking: *Has anyone collected a car number in the one
  hundreds?* Write those on the board. *Who has collected a number
  in the two hundreds?* Write those on the board. Discuss the
  order:
  Why does 309 come before 390?
  Which is the largest possible three-digit car number?
  Which is the smallest possible three-digit car number?
  Discuss numbers like 333.

- **Big Bingo!**
  Paper and pencil for each pair, three dice
  Class activity
  The children work in pairs. Each pair draws four circles on the
  page and writes a different three-digit number in each, e.g.
  324, 445, 162, 366. No numbers should contain a digit more
  than 6.
  Throw all three dice and call out the numbers, e.g. 6, 2 and 3.
  If any pair can make one of their numbers using those digits
  they can cross it out. The winners are the first pair to cross out
  all their numbers.

Section **18**: Negative numbers

Abacus 2
N23

- **Lift journeys**
  A board to draw on
  Class activity
  Draw a lift on the board and next to it a vertical line of
  numbers, from –8 at the bottom to +5 at the top.
  The children work in pairs. Choose a pair and give them a 'lift'
  problem, for example:
  *The lift is at floor 3. It is going down six floors. Where will you be
  when you get out?*
  They can discuss the answer, but only briefly. If they are
  correct they continue the lift journey by choosing another pair
  of children and giving them a problem. They start at the floor
  where the lift last stopped, for example:
  *We are at floor negative 3, and the lift goes up five floors. Where
  will you be then?*
  Continue, giving as many pairs as possible a turn.

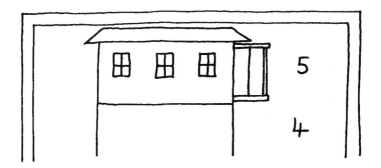

- **I owe you**
  Cubes
  Class activity
  The class plays as a team against you. Choose a child: *You have
  10p and you owe me 14p. How much do you have?* The answer is
  –4p. If that child answers correctly, the class take a cube. The
  first child chooses another to answer a problem. If the first
  child is not correct, you take a cube and choose another child.
  Play until one team has ten cubes.

Section **19**: Difference
(numbers 0 to 10)

Abacus 1
N17

• How much bigger?
A board to write on
Divide the children into two teams.
Ask the first child from each team to write a different number
from 0 to 10 on the board.
The teams take turns to find the difference between the two
numbers.
Check the answers by counting on from the smaller number in
unison. If the answer is correct the team scores a point.
Continue until all the children have had a turn writing a
number.

• How many more?
Ask the children to sit in pairs facing each other.
Choose two numbers between 0 and 10, e.g. 4 and 6.
One child holds up four fingers and the other holds up six
fingers.
The pairs place their hands together and find the difference by
counting the unmatched fingers in unison.
Repeat with other numbers.

• How different?
Class activity
Ask the children to sit in pairs and tell them stories involving
differences. For example:
*The big shark eats six fish. The little shark eats four fish. How
many more has the big shark eaten?*
*The little red chicken ate eight grains of corn but the little yellow
chicken only ate one grain of corn. How many more grains did the
little red chicken eat?*
*The greedy dog ate five bones but the little dog only ate two bones.
How many more did the big dog eat?*
Ask different pairs to answer when they have discussed the
question.

Section **20**: Difference (numbers 0 to 20)

Abacus 2
N20

- **Can you find the difference?**
  Number cards (0 to 20), two cubes
  Place the cards in order in a line.
  Ask the children to sit in a semicircle facing the number line.
  Ask the first child to place the cubes on any two numbers and then ask the next child to find the difference.
  Check by counting on in unison.
  Continue until all children have had a turn.

- **How many differences can you find?**
  Number cards (0 to 20), coloured cubes
  Place the cards in order in a line.
  Ask the children to sit in a semicircle facing the number line.
  If the difference between two numbers is 3 what could the numbers be?
  Choose five children. Each child places two cubes of the same colour on any two numbers where the difference is three.
  Check the answers by counting in unison.
  Repeat for other differences.

- **Stories: differences**
  Class activity
  Ask the children to sit in pairs and tell them stories involving differences. For example:
  The big dog ate fourteen biscuits and the little dog ate ten biscuits. How many more did the big dog eat?
  The first bird ate nine slugs but the second bird ate fifteen slugs. How many more did the second bird eat?
  The first boy knocked down twelve skittles, the second boy knocked down eighteen skittles. How many more did the second boy knock down?
  Ask different pairs to answer when they have discussed the question.

Section **21**: Counting back in tens

Abacus 1
N23

Abacus 2
N14

- **Count down tens**
  Class activity
  Ask the children to sit in a circle.
  Point to a child and say a number, e.g. *fifty-seven*. The children take turns round the circle to reduce the number by ten: *forty-seven, thirty-seven...* Continue until one child reaches 7. The next child chooses a new number and the game continues.

- **Tens stories**
  Ask the children to sit in pairs and tell them stories involving counting back in tens. For example:
  There are 32 children in the class. Ten children cycle to school. How many travel in other ways?
  There are 28 children in the class. Ten children have a packed lunch. How many children eat a school dinner?
  Ask different pairs to answer when they have discussed the question.

- **Throwing tens**
  Ask the children to sit in a circle.
  The first child 'throws' a number by holding his or her hands at chest level and making two fists. Each time a ten is counted the fingers are extended and thrown forward as the child counts aloud. They do this twice for twenty, three times for thirty etc. Individual units are shown after the tens have been thrown.
  For example, if the first child chooses 63, six tens and three units are counted as they are thrown: *ten, twenty, thirty, forty, fifty, sixty, sixty-one, ... sixty-three*.
  The next child reduces the number by ten, counting the number as it is thrown: *ten, twenty, thirty, forty, fifty, fifty-one, ... fifty-three*.
  Continue going round the circle until one child reaches 3.
  The next child chooses a new number and the game continues.

Patterned tens

Large number grid (0 to 99), coloured cubes

A game for 10 children, or 20 pairs

Ask the children to sit in a horseshoe.

Give each pair a cube of the same colour, e.g. all red. The first pair places the cube on any number in the 90s, saying *We have put our number on 97.*

The next pair places their cube on a number 10 less. Continue until all the cubes have been placed. Count back in unison: *ninety-seven, eighty-seven, seventy-seven, ... seven.*

Repeat with another colour and number.

Look at the colour patterns that have been made. Ask: *Why are all the reds in a line, etc?*

Sometimes you may want to record these numbers on the board as the children say them, to emphasise their written form.

Section **22**: Tens and Units

Abacus 1
N6, N11

- **Money tens**
  A board to write on, one 10p coin, nine 1p coins
  You will wish to ensure that the numbers reflect the abilities
  and experiences of the children.
  Divide the children into two teams. The first child from Team
  A writes a number from 10 to 19 on the board. The first child
  from Team B matches the number with the 10p and 1p coins.
  Check the answer by counting on from 10p. If the answer is
  correct Team B score a point.
  Repeat with Team B choosing the number.
  Continue until all the children have taken a turn. The winning
  team gets a clap.

- **Hometime tens**
  To dismiss children at playtime or hometime throw a number
  with your hands, e.g. 14 (one ten and four units) and ask a
  child to say the number.
  Extend this game by throwing a bigger number, e.g. 34 (three
  tens and four units).

- **Ordering numbers**
  Number cards (0 to 10), nine extra copies of the 10 card
  An activity for about 10 children
  Give each child a 10 card and one other. They arrange
  themselves in order, sit down and put their cards on the floor
  and read their numbers, e.g. 10 and 4 is 14.
  Ask questions, for example:
  Which is the smallest number we could make? Why?
  Which is the largest number that we could make? Why?
  Extend this game by giving the children more than one 10
  card.

Three card game

Number cards (0 to 99)

Ask the children to sit in a line (or a horseshoe).
Shuffle the cards and deal three to each child. Ask each child to arrange his or her cards in order. They then work in pairs to arrange their cards in order.
Ask the children to look at their cards. Ask the child who thinks he or she has the smallest number to bring out the card to start a number line.
Ask: *Has anyone a smaller number than this? Who has the next largest number?*
Continue in this way until the line is complete.
How many twenties numbers? How do you know?
Which is the smallest number? Why?
Which is the smallest thirties number? How would this be written?

Building a square

Number cards (0 to 99)

An activity for 10 children (or 10 pairs)
Ask the children to sit in a line. Place cards at random face up on the floor.
Ask each child to collect a set of ten cards, e.g. numbers less than 10 (0-9), forties (40-49).
Ask the children to sit in order with their cards. Ask each to order his or her set of cards and put them in a pile with the smallest number at the top. Ask the children to come out in turn and make a number square:

One child turns away from the square, and another removes a card. The first child turns back and identifies the number which is missing.
Continue until everyone has had a turn.
Extend this activity by removing more than one card.

Section **23**: Multiplication

Twos

Abacus 2
N10, N18

- **Tapping twos**
  Class activity
  You will wish to ensure that younger and less able children
  work with the smaller numbers.
  Ask the children to sit in a circle. The first child stands and
  taps first one foot then the other and says *two*. The next child
  stands and taps first one foot then the other and says *four*.
  Continue until every child has counted their feet in twos.
  Everyone sits down. *Can we do it again more quickly?*
  What about sitting down as we count back in twos?

- **Group twos**
  A PE mat
  Class activity
  This activity is for the beginning or end of a PE lesson.
  Ask the children to get into groups that make two lots of two
  feet and sit down.
  Ask the children to get into groups that make three lots of two
  feet and sit down. Check that they are grouped correctly.
  What about eight feet?
  The children who are not in a group sit on the PE mat until
  the next instruction.

- **Finger twos**
  Class activity
  Ask the children to sit on the carpet and practise counting in twos using fingers up to 10×2 (each finger represents two). In unison count back in twos using fingers.
  Everyone shows 3×2 with fingers. In unison count: *two, four, six*.

- **Dice twos**
  A dice
  Class activity
  Ask the children to sit in a circle. They take turns to throw the dice and find that number of twos, e.g. *six twos are twelve*.

Fives

Abacus 2
N17

- **All the fives**
  Class activity
  Ask the children to sit in pairs ready to use their hands to count in fives.
  The first child in each group begins the chant raising one hand at a time and saying: *five, ten*. The second child continues: *fifteen, twenty*.
  Increase the size of the groups until there are ten children in each and they are quick and confident whatever their position in the group.

- **Counting in fives**
  Class activity
  Ask the children to sit in a circle and use hands to count in fives. As they count the children put their hands palm down on the carpet.

- **Finger fives**
  Class activity
  Ask the children to sit in a circle. Each finger represents a five.
  Raise fingers one at a time and count in unison: *five, ten, fifteen,
  etc.*
  Count back in fives by folding down fingers one at a time: *fifty,
  forty-five, forty, etc.*

Tens

Abacus 2
N13, N18

- **All the tens**
  Class activity
  Ask the children to sit in a circle.
  Use hands to count in unison. The first child puts both hands
  palm down on the carpet and says: *ten*, the next child puts
  both hands down on the carpet and says: *twenty*. Continue
  round the circle.
  Try counting back in tens.

- **Finger tens**
  Class activity
  Ask the children to sit in a circle.
  Each finger represents ten. Count in unison as each finger is
  raised *ten, twenty, etc.*
  Count back in tens, folding down fingers for each number: *one
  hundred, ninety, eighty, etc.*
  One child shows another some fingers, e.g. four. The next child
  says the matching number of tens, i.e. forty. If correct this
  child shows the third child some fingers. Continue until
  everyone has had a turn.

Section **24**: Hundreds, Tens and Units

Abacus 1
N13, N16, N21, N27

Abacus 2
N7

- **Making big numbers**
  One £1, nine 10p, nine 1p coins
  Divide the children into two teams.
  The first child from Team A makes a number with the coins.
  Team B agree the number and say it aloud. If they are correct
  they score a point. Check by counting the coins in unison.
  Team B then make a number, and Team A say what it is.
  You can extend this activity by using more £1 coins.

- **Can you make this?**
  A board to write on
  Ask the children to sit in a circle.
  Write a number on the board, e.g. 127.
  Ask the children to make hand throws to represent their
  number, i.e. each child places one hand on their head once
  (*one hundred*), throws their hands twice (*ten, twenty*) and finally
  raises seven fingers (*seven*).
  Repeat with other numbers.

- **Who wins?**
  **A board to write on, two ten-sided dice (numbered 1
  to 10)**
  Class activity
  Divide the class into two teams. Draw a three-column table for
  each team, headed 'H', 'T', 'U'. Each team throws a ten-sided
  dice, and decides in which column to place the number
  (hundreds, tens or units). Once they have decided they cannot
  move it.
  The teams throw the dice three times. Who has made the
  largest number? That team scores a point. Play until one team
  has scored five points.

Section **25**: Nearest ten

Abacus 2
N16

- **Where shall we go?**
  Number cards (0 to 10), two boxes
  Ask the children to stand in line holding the number cards.
  The child with 0 and the child with 10 stand behind the boxes.
  Ask the other children: *Which box is your number nearest?*
  Where shall we put the number 5?
  We say that 5 is nearest the larger 10.
  This game may be extended by using numbers from 10 to 20 or
  20 to 30.

- **Bean bag fun**
  Bean bags, baskets
  This is a PE activity.
  Ask the children to make a line each holding a bean bag.
  Number the children from 1 to 10. Place one basket in the zero
  position and another in front of 10.
  How quickly can the children put their bag in the nearest ten
  basket?

  This activity can be extended to involve the whole class,
  placing baskets in the zero position and in front of 10, 20 and
  30.
  How quickly can the children put their bean bag in the nearest
  ten basket?

- **Nearest ten?**
  Ask the children to sit in a circle.
  Choose a child and throw them a number, e.g. 27. They say
  the nearest ten i.e. 30. If correct, that child throws a number to
  another. The game continues until everybody has taken a turn.

Section **26**: Sharing

Abacus 2
N19

- **Share it fair**

  Ask the children to sit in pairs and tell them stories involving sharing. For example:

  Mum has six sandwiches for her two children. How many will each child have to eat?

  Dad has six sandwiches for his three children. How many will each child have?

  Mum will share twelve cakes equally among three children. How many will each receive?

  Dad shares twelve cakes equally among four children. How many does each child have? What fraction would that be? How many each for two children?

- **Who's in a hoop?**

  A supply of hoops

  An activity to do during PE.

  Ask twelve children to divide (share) themselves equally among two hoops. *How many children are standing in each hoop?*

  Add two more hoops (to make four).

  Ask the children to divide themselves equally among the four hoops. *How many are standing in each hoop?*

  Repeat for six hoops.

  This activity can be extended with different numbers of children.

  Ask the children which numbers are good for sharing.

- **Finger share**

  Ask the children to sit in a circle.

  In unison the children put all the fingers of both hands together, saying: *ten shared among two hands gives five on each hand.*

  Now they put four fingers on each hand together, saying: *eight shared among two hands gives four on each hand.*

  Continue until all the fingers have been used.

  Extend this activity by sitting the children in pairs, hands touching starting with *twenty fingers shared among two people gives ten each, eighteen fingers shared among two children gives nine each.* Continue until all fingers have been used.

Section **27**: Halving

Abacus 2
N27

- **Keep halving**
  Ask the children to sit in a circle. Give the first child a number,
  e.g. *sixteen*. The first child halves it (*eight*), and the next child
  halves that (*four*). Continue as far as you can.
  Repeat for a different number. Discuss why some numbers are
  better for halving than others.

- **How many in your half?**
  Ask the children to sit in a circle and ask six to sit down in the
  middle. Ask half of the six to stand on one leg. Ask the others:
  *How many are standing on one leg? How many are still sitting
  down?*
  Repeat with other numbers and actions.

- **Halving stories**
  Class activity
  Ask the children to sit in pairs and tell them stories involving
  halving. For example:
  *There are twelve sweets in a packet. Mary has eaten half of them.
  How many sweets are left?*
  *There are ten children playing in the park. Half the children are on
  the roundabout. How many children are on the roundabout?*
  *There are eight teddies on the bed, half have brown fur and half
  have golden fur. How many teddies have brown fur?*
  Ask different pairs for the answers.

Section **28**: Fractions

Abacus 1
N8

Abacus 2
N27

- **Can you jump a fraction?**
  An activity to do during PE.
  Everyone, including you, stands facing one wall. Raise your right hand and say: *We are going to jump a $\frac{1}{4}$ turn to the right. What will we now be looking at?* Everyone jump $\frac{1}{4}$ turn to the right.
  Continue jumping quarter turns until you have jumped round in a full circle. When the children become confident try $\frac{1}{2}$ turns, $\frac{3}{4}$ turns and full turns. Always ask: *What should we be looking at?* before jumping the fraction.
  Ask questions, e.g. *How many $\frac{1}{4}$ turns in a $\frac{3}{4}$ turn?*

- **What is your fraction doing?**
  An activity to do during PE.
  Arrange the children in groups of four, eight, twelve or sixteen. Give instructions, for example:

  $\frac{1}{4}$ *of the children in each group stand on one leg.*

  $\frac{1}{2}$ *of the children in each group hop.*

  $\frac{3}{4}$ *of the children in each group jump up and down.*

  All the children in each group sit very quietly.

- **How many will they have?**
  Ask the children to sit in pairs and tell them stories involving fractions. For example:
  Imagine a plate with eight cakes. John ate a quarter of them. How many did he eat? How many were left?
  Imagine eight cakes again. The naughty dog ate four cakes. What fraction did the dog eat?
  Mum went shopping and bought twelve eggs (one dozen). She dropped them. Luckily only $\frac{1}{4}$ broke. How many eggs broke? What fraction were whole?
  Ask different pairs for the answers.

Section **29**: Pattern

Abacus R   **Abacus 2**
N16   N10, N11, N17, N18

- **Let's make a pattern**
  Class activity
  Ask all the children to sit in a line (or horseshoe).
  The first child stands, the second child stays sitting, the third
  child stands. *Can we carry on with the pattern?*
  Ask the children to sit again quietly. *Who can think of another
  pattern?* e.g. two standing, two sitting. *What comes next?*
  Repeat for other patterns, e.g. one standing, three sitting.
  Read the patterns in unison.

- **Hand Patterns**
  Class activity
  Ask the children to sit in a circle.
  The first child places five fingers on the carpet palm down, the
  second child places ten fingers, the third child five fingers.
  What comes next? Can we carry on the pattern?
  Can we say the pattern in unison?
  Who can choose another pattern? e.g. four fingers then six fingers.

- **Musical Patterns**
  Class activity
  Ask the children to sit in a circle.
  The first child claps once, the second child taps a foot once,
  the third child claps once. Continue the pattern round the
  circle. Repeat for other patterns, e.g.
  – clap, clap, tap, clap, clap, tap, ...
  – tap head once, shoulder twice, head once, shoulder twice, ...
  Invent other patterns.

- **Counting Patterns**
  Class activity
  Ask the children to sit in a circle. They take turns to count on
  in threes: *zero, three, six, nine etc.* Repeat for twos, fours, fives,
  tens. Try a mixed pattern, e.g.
  – count on two, count on four, count on two, count on four, ...
  – count on two, back one, count on two, back one, ...
  Continue the pattern round the circle.
  Ask the children to suggest their own patterns.